CHOOSE BRAVE

LOVEGODGREATLY.COM

CHOOSE BRAVE

Copyright © 2018 by Love God Greatly Ministry

Published in Dallas by Love God Greatly.

Special thanks to:
Photos from: unsplash.com
Recipes from: *Huisgenoot: Wenresepte 3,* by Annette Human, Human & Rousseau Cape Town, 1987

Unless otherwise noted, Scripture quotations are taken from *The Holy Bible, English Standard Version* Copyright © 2001 by Crossway Bibles, a publishing ministry of Good News Publishers.

Printed in the United States of America

Library of Congress Cataloging-in-Publication Data

Printed in the United States of America

23 22 21 20 19 18

6 5 4 3 2 1

AT LOVE GOD GREATLY, YOU'LL FIND REAL, AUTHENTIC WOMEN. WOMEN WHO ARE IMPERFECT, YET FORGIVEN.

Women who desire less of us, and a whole lot more of Jesus. Women who long to know God through His Word, because we know that Truth transforms and sets us free. Women who are better together, saturated in God's Word and in community with one another.

Welcome, friend. We're so glad you're here...

CONTENTS

WELCOME

We are glad you have decided to join us in this Bible study! First of all, please know that you have been prayed for! It is not a coincidence you are participating in this study.

Our prayer for you is simple: that you will grow closer to our Lord as you dig into His Word each and every day! As you develop the discipline of being in God's Word on a daily basis, our prayer is that you will fall in love with Him even more as you spend time reading from the Bible.

Each day before you read the assigned Scripture(s), pray and ask God to help you understand it. Invite Him to speak to you through His Word. Then listen. It's His job to speak to you, and it's your job to listen and obey.

Take time to read the verses over and over again. We are told in Proverbs to search and you will find: "Search for it like silver, and hunt for it like hidden treasure. Then you will understand" (Prov. 2:4–5 NCV).

All of us here at Love God Greatly can't wait for you to get started, and we hope to see you at the finish line. Endure, persevere, press on—and don't give up! Finish well what you are beginning today. We will be here every step of the way, cheering you on! We are in this together. Fight to rise early, to push back the stress of the day, to sit alone and spend time in God's Word! Let's see what God has in store for you in this study! Journey with us as we learn to love God greatly with our lives!

As you go through this study, join us in the following resources below:

Weekly Blog Posts •

Weekly Memory Verses •

Weekly Challenges •

Facebook, Twitter, Instagram •

LoveGodGreatly.com •

Hashtags: #LoveGodGreatly •

RESOURCES

Join Us

ONLINE

lovegodgreatly.com

STORE

lovegodgreatly.com/store

FACEBOOK

facebook.com/LoveGodGreatly

INSTAGRAM

instagram.com/lovegodgreatlyofficial

TWITTER

@_LoveGodGreatly

DOWNLOAD THE APP

CONTACT US

info@lovegodgreatly.com

CONNECT

#LoveGodGreatly

LOVE
GOD
GREATLY

Love God Greatly (LGG) is a beautiful community of women who use a variety of technology platforms to keep each other accountable in God's Word. We start with a simple Bible reading plan, but it doesn't stop there.

Some women gather in homes and churches locally, while others connect online with women across the globe. Whatever the method, we lovingly lock arms and unite for this purpose: to love God greatly with our lives.

Would you consider reaching out and doing this study with someone?

In today's fast-paced technology-driven world, it would be easy to study God's Word in an isolated environment that lacks encouragement or support, but that isn't the intention here at Love God Greatly. God created us to live in community with Him and with those around us.

We need each other, and we live life better together. Because of this, would you consider reaching out and doing this study with someone?

Rest assured we'll be studying right alongside you—learning with you, cheering for you, enjoying sweet fellowship, and smiling from ear to ear as we watch God unite women together—intentionally connecting hearts and minds for His glory.

So here's the challenge: call your mom, your sister, your grandma, the girl across the street, or the college friend across the country. Gather a group of girls from your church or workplace, or meet in a coffee shop with friends you have always wished you knew better.

Arm-in-arm and hand-in-hand, let's do this thing…together.

SOAP STUDY
HOW AND WHY TO SOAP

In this study we offer you a study journal to accompany the verses we are reading. This journal is designed to help you interact with God's Word and learn to dig deeper, encouraging you to slow down and reflect on what God is saying to you that day.

At Love God Greatly, we use the SOAP Bible study method. Before beginning, let's take a moment to define this method and share why we recommend using it during your quiet time in the following pages.

It's one thing to simply read Scripture. But when you interact with it, intentionally slowing down to really reflect on it, suddenly words start popping off the page. The SOAP method allows you to dig deeper into Scripture and see more than you would if you simply read the verses and then went on your merry way.

The most important ingredients in the SOAP method are your interaction with God's Word and your application of His Word to your life:

Blessed is the one who does not walk in step with the wicked or stand in the way that sinners take or sit in the company of mockers, but whose delight is in the law of the LORD, and who meditates on his law day and night. That person is like a tree planted by streams of water, which yields its fruit in season and whose leaf does not wither—whatever they do prospers.
(Ps. 1:1–3, NIV)

Please take the time to SOAP through our Bible studies and see for yourself how much more you get from your daily reading.

You'll be amazed.

The most important ingredients in the SOAP method are your interaction with God's Word and your application of His Word to your life.

SOAP STUDY *(CONTINUED)*
WHAT DOES SOAP MEAN?

S STANDS FOR
SCRIPTURE

Physically write out the verses.

You'll be amazed at what God will reveal to you just by taking the time to slow down and write out what you are reading!

MONDAY

READ
Colossians 1:5–8

SOAP
Colossians 1:5–8

Scripture

WRITE
OUT THE
SCRIPTURE
PASSAGE
FOR THE
DAY.

This faith and love that spring from the hope stored up for you in heaven and about which you have already heard in the true message of the gospel that has come to you. In the same way, the gospel is bearing fruit and growing throughout the whole world just as it has been doing among you since the day you heard it and truly understood God's grace. You learned it from Epaphras, our dear fellow servant, who is a faithful minister of Christ on our behalf, and who also told us of your love in the Spirit.

Observations

WRITE
DOWN 1 OR 2
OBSERVATIONS
FROM THE
PASSAGE.

When you combine faith and love, you get hope. We must remember that our hope is in heaven; it is yet to come. The gospel is the Word of truth. The gospel is continually bearing fruit and growing from the first day to the last. It just takes one person to change a whole community, Epaphras.

O STANDS FOR
OBSERVATION

What do you see in the verses that you're reading?

Who is the intended audience? Is there a repetition of words?

What words stand out to you?

A STANDS FOR
APPLICATION

*This is when God's
Word becomes
personal.*

*What is God
saying to you today?*

*How can you apply
what you just read
to your own personal
life?*

*What changes do you
need to make? Is there
action you need to
take?*

Applications

WRITE
DOWN 1 OR 2
APPLICATIONS
FROM THE
PASSAGE.

God used one man, Epaphras, to change a whole town. I was reminded that we are simply called to tell others about Christ; it's God's job to spread the gospel, to grow it, and have it bear fruit. I felt today's verses were almost directly spoken to Love God Greatly women. The gospel is bearing fruit and growing throughout the whole world just as it has been doing among you since the day you heard it and truly understood God's grace.

Pray

WRITE OUT
A PRAYER
OVER WHAT
YOU LEARNED
FROM TODAY'S
PASSAGE.

Dear Lord, please help me to be an Epaphras, to tell others about You and then leave the results in Your loving hands. Please help me to understand and apply personally what I have read today to my life, thereby becoming more and more like You each and every day. Help me to live a life that bears the fruit of faith and love, anchoring my hope in heaven, not here on earth. Help me to remember that the best is yet to come!

P STANDS FOR **PRAYER**

Pray God's Word back to Him. Spend time thanking Him.

If He has revealed something to you during this time in His Word, pray about it.

If He has revealed some sin that is in your life, confess. And remember, He loves you dearly.

A RECIPE FOR YOU

MILK TART

Crust

1/2 packet (100 g or 1/2 cup) crumbled Maria cookies or graham cracker crumbs

75 g (80 ml or 2/3 cup) melted margarine

15 ml sugar (1 Tbsp)

1 ml cinnamon (1/4 tsp)

Filling

500 ml (2 cups) milk

40 g (50 ml or 1/3 cup) margarine

100 g (125 ml or 1/2 cup) sugar

2 ml (1/2 tsp) salt

30 ml (2 Tbsp) flour

30 ml (2 Tbsp) cornstarch

2 large eggs, separated

5 ml (1 tsp) vanilla

cinnamon

Directions

- Mix all crust ingredients together and press into the bottom of pie plate. (A store-bought pie shell or small tart shells can also be used.)

- Bring milk, margarine, sugar, and salt to boil in a large pot over low heat. Stir often.

- Mix flour and cornstarch with a little bit of extra cold milk to form a smooth paste.

- Beat egg yolks and add to the paste.

- Mix a little bit of the boiling milk mixture with the egg mixture and then add it all to the rest of the milk mixture in the pot while stirring.

- Heat for a few minutes while stirring, until the mixture becomes thick.

- Remove from heat and add the vanilla.

- Beat egg whites until they form soft peaks and fold into the milk mixture.

- Pour the filling into the baking dish or pie shell.

- Sprinkle with cinnamon.

- Cool for a few minutes and then let the tart cool completely in the fridge.

- Keep in fridge.

- Enjoy!

LGG AFRIKAANS TESTIMONIES

BIANKA, SOUTH AFRICA

What Love God Greatly means to me is hard to put into words because the feelings are so overwhelming. As I write this, the tears are rolling down my face because this Bible Study saved my life in Christ.

When my husband left me for another woman, I was shattered. I prayed and read every Bible Study that I could lay my hands on to try and make sense of this explosion in my life. God sent me a piece on Facebook that came out of a Love God Greatly study. Then I saw that there was a group that I could belong to and that we could ask for prayer. This was exactly what I was looking for! Velia started praying for me, together with so many others, and the Lord's intervention has been clearly visible in every breath I take.

My healing started here.

I started at the end of Week 3 of the Promises of God study and followed the study on Facebook. Initially I didn't fully understand how the study worked, or what SOAP meant. When we were notified that we could now download the new Savior Bible Study materials, I noticed all the materials for the other studies. Everything that was posted on the Love God Greatly Afrikaans Facebook page has helped so much that I decided to download the Savior and Promises of God study materials.

I prayed and pleaded that God would intervene and show me that He is there for me, that I am not too late, and that He didn't also leave me. The next morning His answer was: Isaiah 41:10: "So do not fear, for I am with you; do not be dismayed, for I am your God. I will strengthen you and help you; I will uphold you with my righteous right hand."

How much more could I want Him to spell it out to me? My healing started here. I was looking for the Lifesaver and I was swimming and trying to keep my head above the water. Then He lifted me out and now I am sitting at His feet, today and every day.

I do most of my Bible studies in English, but Afrikaans remains my mother tongue. Is the Father's Word not more profound when He speaks to you in your mother tongue?

MARTIE, SOUTH AFRICA

The fact that I can read these studies in Afrikaans means so much to me. It means that I understand what I read so much better. Lots of Bible Studies are in English, and because English is not my mother tongue, I regularly have to look up a word or two or three in the dictionary to see what it means so that I can grasp and understand the true meaning.

In addition to the benefits of having these studies in my own language, these studies enrich my life so much. I learn a lot about myself, I do introspection, and see where I do wrong. A person is inclined to only notice one thing and miss or lose sight of another aspect - I think specifically about the Jonah study. I have always just looked at Jonah as someone who didn't want to listen to God, and then he was punished. But for the first time I realized that I am also a Jonah, because I also don't want to listen to God at times.

I am a woman of God, God notices me, He will never leave me...

The other thing I love is getting the studies via email. That means that I can always go back to a study and read something again. I can remind myself again that I am a woman of God, God notices me, He will never leave me, He sees the tears, the suffering and worries, and yet He cares for me every day! I have learned again to give all my worries to God - He carries my worries better than I could. I have learned again what it means not to worry about tomorrow, it is not promised, and only God's love is promised for today and every day for the rest of my life. I have learned to just live for today. But above all, I have learned that it doesn't matter what anybody says or thinks, all that matters is God!

To connect with LGG Afrikaans Branch:

- liefgodgrootliks@gmail.com
- liefgodgrootliks.wordpress.com
- facebook.com/Love-God-Greatly-Afrikaans-717623225000335

Do you know someone who could use our *Love God Greatly* Bible studies in Afrikaans? If so, make sure and tell them about LGG Afrikaans and all the amazing Bible study resources we provide to help equip them with God's Word!!!

CHOOSE BRAVE

Let's Begin

INTRODUCTION

CHOOSE BRAVE

"Have I not commanded you? Be strong and courageous. Do not be afraid; do not be discouraged, for the LORD your God will be with you wherever you go." – Joshua 1:9

We all like stories of bravery and heroism because in that hero or heroine we see something that we lack but desire. We see someone who is noble or bold, righteous or daring, and we wish we could be like that.

Many, if not all of us, have experienced fear that has kept us from taking an unknown road. We know the kind of weakness that can make us give up or not even try. We also have experienced cowardice that makes us doubt, feel overwhelmed, and turn away from what God would have us do. So, when we read or watch stories of heroism and bravery we cheer and even tear up a bit. When we watch someone have courage in the midst of fear, undaunted in the midst of adversity, and resolute in the midst of weakness we are inspired to be brave ourselves.

But this bravery is usually short-lived because earthly motivation can only take us so far. We need a bravery that holds up through even the scariest and most difficult of circumstances. We need the kind of bravery that derives its power from the God who knows no fear, who holds all power and goodness, and who freely gives these things to those who ask in faith.

In Joshua 1:9 God gives Joshua the command to be strong and courageous, to not be afraid or discouraged. Why? Because God promises that He would be with Joshua wherever he went. This is the same promise God made to Abraham (Gen. 26:3), Jacob (Gen. 31:3), Moses (Ex. 3:12), the people of Israel (Is. 41:10), and to you (Matthew 28:20).

Throughout your life you will face many things that require bravery, and, in this study, we will look at a number of these areas and how we can find boldness in God. Some displays of bravery will require small little leaps while others will ask us to scale seemingly gigantic mountains. But we are never asked to muster up bravery out of our own strength.

When you feel like you don't have the wisdom to make certain decisions remember that you have a God who has all wisdom – you just need to ask. If you feel that you have no strength for the day ahead, remember that you have the strength of your almighty God at your disposal. You just need to cry out to Him. If you feel that you are lacking the courage to take the next step, remember that God is on your side, fighting for and with you, and is willing and able to give you everything you need (2 Peter 1:3).

It takes a lot of courage to live a life of light in a world of darkness, to overcome evil with good, and to live out true faith in front of those who mock and blaspheme God. But God never asks you to take on this life on your own. Be strong and courageous, live boldly and without fear, because the Lord is with you wherever you go.

Looking to Jesus,

Jen

READING PLAN

WEEK 1

Monday - Brave to fight the good fight
READ: 1 Timothy 6:6-16; Ephesians 6:10-17
SOAP: 1 Timothy 6:11-12

Tuesday - Brave to trust
READ: Proverbs 3:5-6; Psalm 9:10; Psalm 20:7
SOAP: Proverbs 3:5-6, Psalm 9:10

Wednesday - Brave to do good
READ: Galatians 6:9; Ephesians 2:10; Psalm 34:8
SOAP: Psalm 34:8

Thursday - Brave in forgiving
READ: Matthew 18:21-22; Colossians 3:13
SOAP: Colossians 3:13

Friday - Brave in facing your fears
READ: John 14:27; Psalm 118:6; Isaiah 41:10
SOAP: Isaiah 41:10

WEEK 2

Monday - Brave to fear God over man
READ: Proverbs 1:7; Proverbs 8:13; Proverbs 29:25
SOAP: Proverbs 29:25

Tuesday - Brave in resting in God
READ: Hebrews 4:9-10; Psalm 116:7; Jeremiah 6:16
SOAP: Hebrews 4:9-10

Wednesday - Brave to obey God
READ: Deuteronomy 11:1; John 15:9-14
SOAP: Deuteronomy 11:1

Thursday - Brave in uncertainty
READ: Matthew 6:25-34; Matthew 11:28-30
SOAP: Matthew 11:28-30

Friday - Brave in showing hospitality
READ: Romans 12:13; 1 Peter 4:9; Hebrews 13:16
SOAP: Romans 12:13

WEEK 3

Monday - Brave in the face of persecution
READ: Matthew 5:10, 44; Romans 8:35-39; Psalm 27:1
SOAP: Romans 8:35-37

Tuesday - Brave to be generous
READ: 2 Corinthians 9:6-8; Proverbs 19:17
SOAP: 2 Corinthians 9:6-8

Wednesday - Brave to live counter-culturally
READ: Romans 12:1-3
SOAP: Romans 12:2

Thursday - Brave to speak truth
READ: Ephesians 4:25; Proverbs 12:17; John 17:17
SOAP: Ephesians 4:25

Friday - Brave when discouraged
READ: 2 Corinthians 4:8-9; Mark 10:27
SOAP: 2 Corinthians 4:8-9

WEEK 4

Monday - Brave in the midst of loss
READ: Psalm 147:3; Psalm 55:22; Revelation 21:4
SOAP: Revelation 21:4

Tuesday - Brave in weakness
READ: Romans 12:1-10; Psalm 73:26; Romans 8:26;
SOAP: Psalm 73:26

Wednesday - Brave during temptations
READ: 1 Peter 5:8-9; 1 Corinthians 10:13; Hebrews 4:15-16
SOAP: Hebrews 4:15-16

Thursday - Brave during trials
READ: James 1:2-4; Psalm 34:19
SOAP: James 1:2-4

Friday - Brave to walk forward in faith
READ: Hebrews 11:1; 2 Corinthians 4:18; Mark 9:14-24
SOAP: Mark 9:24

WEEK 5

Monday - Brave to encourage/exhort the body of Christ
READ: Hebrews 10:23-25; Proverbs 27:17
SOAP: Hebrews 10:24

Tuesday - Brave in love
READ: John 13:34-35; 1 John 4:19-21
SOAP: John 13:34-35

Wednesday - Brave to use your gifts
READ: 1 Peter 4:8-10; 1 Corinthians 12:4-7
SOAP: 1 Corinthians 12:4-7

Thursday - Be brave in prayer
READ: 1 John 5:14; Ephesians 6:18; Matthew 21:22; Luke 18:1
SOAP: 1 John 5:14

Friday - Brave in your calling
READ: 1 Peter 2:9; Ephesians 2:10
SOAP: Ephesians 2:10

WEEK 6

Monday - Brave to put God first
READ: Matthew 6:33; Deuteronomy 6:4-9
SOAP: Deuteronomy 6:4-6

Tuesday - Brave in smashing idols
READ: Exodus 20:1-3; Isaiah 44:6-20
SOAP: Exodus 20:1-3

Wednesday - Brave in putting others first
READ: Philippians 2:1-11
SOAP: Philippians 2:3-5

Thursday - Brave in pursuit of holiness
READ: 1 Peter 1:14-19
SOAP: 1 Peter 1:15-16

Friday - Brave to reach others
READ: Matthew 28:19-20; Romans 10:14-15
SOAP: Matthew 28:19-20

YOUR
GOALS

We believe it's important to write out goals for this study. Take some time now and write three goals you would like to focus on as you begin to rise each day and dig into God's Word. Make sure and refer back to these goals throughout the next weeks to help you stay focused. You can do it!

1. To be closer to the Lord by studying His word

2. To become stronger and more brave by studying about being brave

3. Be more disciplined in Bible study by digging deeper into the word

Signature: Carol Morris

Date: 2/17/19

I started the study before today, but I'm just now paying attention to this page

23

WEEK 1

Fight the good fight of the faith. Take hold of the eternal life to which you were called and about which you made the good confession in the presence of many witnesses.

1 TIMOTHY 6:12

PRAYER

WRITE DOWN YOUR PRAYER REQUESTS
AND PRAISES FOR EACH DAY.

Prayer focus for this week:
Spend time praying for your family members.

MONDAY

TUESDAY

WEDNESDAY

THURSDAY

FRIDAY

CHALLENGE

You can find this listed in our Monday blog post.

MONDAY
Scripture for Week 1

1 Timothy 6:6-16

6 But godliness with contentment is great gain, 7 for we brought nothing into the world, and we cannot take anything out of the world. 8 But if we have food and clothing, with these we will be content. 9 But those who desire to be rich fall into temptation, into a snare, into many senseless and harmful desires that plunge people into ruin and destruction. 10 For the love of money is a root of all kinds of evils. It is through this craving that some have wandered away from the faith and pierced themselves with many pangs.

11 But as for you, O man of God, flee these things. Pursue righteousness, godliness, faith, love, steadfastness, gentleness. 12 Fight the good fight of the faith. Take hold of the eternal life to which you were called and about which you made the good confession in the presence of many witnesses. 13 I charge you in the presence of God, who gives life to all things, and of Christ Jesus, who in his testimony before Pontius Pilate made the good confession, 14 to keep the commandment unstained and free from reproach until the appearing of our Lord Jesus Christ, 15 which he will display at the proper time—he who is the blessed and only Sovereign, the King of kings and Lord of lords, 16 who alone has immortality, who dwells in unapproachable light, whom no one has ever seen or can see. To him be honor and eternal dominion. Amen.

Ephesians 6:10-17

10 Finally, be strong in the Lord and in the strength of his might. 11 Put on the whole armor of God, that you may be able to stand against the schemes of the devil.12 For we do not wrestle against flesh and blood, but against the rulers, against the authorities, against the cosmic powers over this present darkness, against the spiritual forces of evil in the heavenly places. 13 Therefore take up the whole armor of God, that you may be able to withstand in the evil day, and having done all, to stand firm. 14 Stand therefore, having fastened on the belt of truth, and having put on the breastplate of righteousness, 15 and, as shoes for your feet, having put on the readiness given by the gospel of peace. 16 In all circumstances take up the shield of faith, with which you can extinguish all the flaming darts of the evil one;17 and take the helmet of salvation, and the sword of the Spirit, which is the word of God.

MONDAY

READ:
1 Timothy 6:6-16; Ephesians 6:10-17

SOAP:
1 Timothy 6:11-12

Scripture

WRITE
OUT THE
SCRIPTURE
PASSAGE
FOR THE
DAY.

"But you, man of God, flee from all this, and pursue righteousness, godliness, faith, love, endurance, and gentleness. Fight the good fight of faith. Take hold of eternal life to which you were called when you made your good confession in the presence of many witnesses." NIV

Observations

WRITE
DOWN 1 OR 2
OBSERVATIONS
FROM THE
PASSAGE.

Applications

WRITE DOWN 1 OR 2 APPLICATIONS FROM THE PASSAGE.

Pray

WRITE OUT A PRAYER OVER WHAT YOU LEARNED FROM TODAY'S PASSAGE.

Lord,

I pray that me and my family members will flee from temptation and that we will all pursue righteousness, godliness, faith, love, endurance, and gentleness. Fight the good fight of faith, take hold of eternal life. (help us to)

In Jesus name

TUESDAY
Scripture for Week 1

Proverbs 3:5-6
5 Trust in the Lord with all your heart,
  and do not lean on your own understanding.
6 In all your ways acknowledge him,
  and he will make straight your paths.

Psalm 9:10
10 And those who know your name put their trust in you,
  for you, O Lord, have not forsaken those who seek you.

Psalm 20:7
7 Some trust in chariots and some in horses,
  but we trust in the name of the Lord our God.

TUESDAY

READ:
Proverbs 3:5-6; Psalm 9:10; Psalm 20:7

SOAP:
Proverbs 3:5-6, Psalm 9:10

Scripture

WRITE
OUT THE
SCRIPTURE
PASSAGE
FOR THE
DAY.

Prov. 3:5-6
" Trust in the Lord with all your
heart, and do not lean on your
own understanding. In all
your ways acknowledge him, and
he will make your paths straight."

Psalm 9:10
" And those who know your name put
their trust in you; for you, O Lord,
have not forsaken those who
seek you."

Observations

WRITE
DOWN 1 OR 2
OBSERVATIONS
FROM THE
PASSAGE.

- Those who know Him trust
  Him
- If we acknowledge Him in
  all our ways He will make
  our paths straight.

WRITE DOWN 1 OR 2 APPLICATIONS FROM THE PASSAGE.

At times I feel forsaken b/c I've been in this crazy situation in my marriage for so long, but the Lord says He does not forsake those who seek Him.

Pray

WRITE OUT A PRAYER OVER WHAT YOU LEARNED FROM TODAY'S PASSAGE.

Dear Lord,
I pray I will trust you with all my heart and lean not to my own understanding, but in all my ways acknowledge you and you will make my paths straight. Help me, Lord, to know you better so that I can trust you more. Thank you that you do not forsake those who seek you. In Jesus' name

WEDNESDAY

Galatians 6:9

9 And let us not grow weary of doing good, for in due season we will reap, if we do not give up.

Ephesians 2:10

10 For we are his workmanship, created in Christ Jesus for good works, which God prepared beforehand, that we should walk in them.

Psalm 34:8

Oh, taste and see that the Lord is good!
   Blessed is the man who takes refuge in him!

WEDNESDAY

READ:
Galatians 6:9; Ephesians 2:10; Psalm 34:8

SOAP:
Psalm 34:8

Scripture

WRITE
OUT THE
SCRIPTURE
PASSAGE
FOR THE
DAY.

"Taste and see that the Lord is good; blessed is the one who takes refuge in Him."

Observations

WRITE
DOWN 1 OR 2
OBSERVATIONS
FROM THE
PASSAGE.

The Lord is good

WRITE
DOWN 1 OR 2
APPLICATIONS
FROM THE
PASSAGE.

Blessed is the person who takes refuge in Him

Pray

WRITE OUT
A PRAYER
OVER WHAT
YOU LEARNED
FROM TODAY'S
PASSAGE.

Dear Lord,
I have tasted your presence and it is good, you are good. Please help me to find/take refuge in you so that I will be blessed.
In Jesus Name

THURSDAY
Scripture for Week 1

Matthew 18:21-22
21 Then Peter came up and said to him, "Lord, how often will my brother sin against me, and I forgive him? As many as seven times?" 22 Jesus said to him, "I do not say to you seven times, but seventy-seven times.

Colossians 3:13
13 bearing with one another and, if one has a complaint against another, forgiving each other; as the Lord has forgiven you, so you also must forgive.

THURSDAY

READ:
Matthew 18:21-22; Colossians 3:13

SOAP:
Colossians 3:13

Scripture

WRITE
OUT THE
SCRIPTURE
PASSAGE
FOR THE
DAY.

"make allowance for each other's faults, and forgive anyone who offends you. Remember, the Lord forgave you, so you must forgive others."

Observations

WRITE
DOWN 1 OR 2
OBSERVATIONS
FROM THE
PASSAGE.

- make allowance for each other's faults
- forgive them b/c the Lord forgave me

WRITE
DOWN 1 OR 2
APPLICATIONS
FROM THE
PASSAGE.

I must forgive b/c
I have been forgiven

Pray

WRITE OUT
A PRAYER
OVER WHAT
YOU LEARNED
FROM TODAY'S
PASSAGE.

Dear Lord,
Help me to make
allowance for other
people's faults and my
own too. Please help
me to forgive them
and myself b/c you
have forgiven me.
In Jesus Name

FRIDAY
Scripture for Week 1

John 14:27
27 Peace I leave with you; my peace I give to you. Not as the world gives do I give to you. Let not your hearts be troubled, neither let them be afraid.

Psalm 118:6
6The Lord is on my side; I will not fear.
    What can man do to me?

Isaiah 41:10
10 fear not, for I am with you;
    be not dismayed, for I am your God;
I will strengthen you, I will help you,
    I will uphold you with my righteous right hand.

FRIDAY

READ:
John 14:27; Psalm 118:6; Isaiah 41:10

SOAP:
Isaiah 41:10

Scripture

WRITE
OUT THE
SCRIPTURE
PASSAGE
FOR THE
DAY.

" Fear not, for I am with you; be not dismayed, for I am your God; I will strengthen you, I will help you, I will uphold you with my righteous right hand. "

Observations

WRITE
DOWN 1 OR 2
OBSERVATIONS
FROM THE
PASSAGE.

- Fear not b/c God is with me
- Do not be dismayed (lose courage or resolution) (or discouraged) for He is my God.
- He will strengthen me
- He will help me
- He will hold me up with His victorious right hand

WRITE
DOWN 1 OR 2
APPLICATIONS
FROM THE
PASSAGE.

I don't have to be afraid b/c the Lord is with me. I don't have to be discouraged b/c ~~God~~ He is my God and He will strengthen me (to do what I need to do) and help me (with what I need to be doing) He will hold me up (even when I don't feel strong) with His victorious right hand.
Hallelujah!!!

Pray

WRITE OUT
A PRAYER
OVER WHAT
YOU LEARNED
FROM TODAY'S
PASSAGE.

Lord,
Please help me to not be afraid because you are with me. Not be discouraged because you are my God and nothing is impossible for you. Thank you Lord that you strengthen me when I need it and you help me when I need it (which is all the time - pretty much every day I need Him to strengthen me + help me). Thank you that you hold me up with your victorious right hand. In Jesus name,
Amen 41

REFLECTION
QUESTIONS

1. What does it mean to "fight the good fight of faith?" How do we fight?

2. What are some things you trust in besides the Lord? How does trusting the Lord require bravery?

3. Why can doing good be exhausting or frustrating? We were created for good works. How should this truth affect all you do? What does God's goodness mean for your life?

4. What makes forgiveness hard? Why do you think there is such an emphasis in the Bible about forgiving others?

   Because what they have done hurt me. There is so much emphasis in the Bible b/c we will always have people to forgive and holding on to resentment hurts us and the Lord said we must forgive.

5. What are some of your fears? What truths about God combat these fears? In what distinct ways do the Father, Son, and Holy Spirit help you?

NOTES

WEEK 2

You shall therefore love the LORD your God and keep his charge, his statutes, his rules, and his commandments always.

DEUTERONOMY 11:1

PRAYER

WRITE DOWN YOUR PRAYER REQUESTS
AND PRAISES FOR EACH DAY.

Prayer focus for this week:
Spend time praying for your country.

MONDAY

TUESDAY

WEDNESDAY

THURSDAY

FRIDAY

CHALLENGE

You can find this listed in our Monday blog post.

MONDAY
Scripture for Week 2

Proverbs 1:7
7 The fear of the Lord is the beginning of knowledge;
  fools despise wisdom and instruction.

Proverbs 8:13
13 The fear of the Lord is hatred of evil.
Pride and arrogance and the way of evil
  and perverted speech I hate.

Proverbs 29:25
25 The fear of man lays a snare,
  but whoever trusts in the Lord is safe.

MONDAY

READ:
Proverbs 1:7; Proverbs 8:13; Proverbs 29:25

SOAP:
Proverbs 29:25

Scripture

WRITE
OUT THE
SCRIPTURE
PASSAGE
FOR THE
DAY.

" Fearing people is a dangerous trap, but trusting the Lord means safety " NLT

Observations

WRITE
DOWN 1 OR 2
OBSERVATIONS
FROM THE
PASSAGE.

Fearing people is dangerous
Fearing people is a trap
Trusting the Lord is safe

WRITE
DOWN 1 OR 2
APPLICATIONS
FROM THE
PASSAGE.

If I fear people it is a dangerous trap, but if I trust the Lord I will be safe.

Pray

WRITE OUT
A PRAYER
OVER WHAT
YOU LEARNED
FROM TODAY'S
PASSAGE.

Dear Lord,
Please help me to not fear people or put my trust in them, but put my trust in you instead because then I know I will be safe. Thank you Lord!
In Jesus Name,
Amen

TUESDAY
Scripture for Week 2

Hebrews 4:9-10
9 So then, there remains a Sabbath rest for the people of
God, 10 for whoever has entered God's rest has also rested from his
works as God did from his.

Psalm 116:7
7 Return, O my soul, to your rest;
    for the Lord has dealt bountifully with you.

Jeremiah 6:16
16 Thus says the Lord:
"Stand by the roads, and look,
    and ask for the ancient paths,
where the good way is; and walk in it,
    and find rest for your souls.
But they said, 'We will not walk in it.'

TUESDAY

READ:
Hebrews 4:9-10; Psalm 116:7; Jeremiah 6:16

SOAP:
Hebrews 4:9-10

Scripture

WRITE
OUT THE
SCRIPTURE
PASSAGE
FOR THE
DAY.

"So then, there remains a Sabbath rest for the people of God, for whoever has entered God's rest has also rested from his works as God did from His."

Observations

WRITE
DOWN 1 OR 2
OBSERVATIONS
FROM THE
PASSAGE.

- There is a Sabbath rest for the people of God
- whoever enters God's rest has rested from his works just as God did from His.

WRITE
DOWN 1 OR 2
APPLICATIONS
FROM THE
PASSAGE.

Resting on the Sabbath is entering into God's rest b/c He also rested on the Sabbath

Pray

WRITE OUT
A PRAYER
OVER WHAT
YOU LEARNED
FROM TODAY'S
PASSAGE.

Dear Lord,
    Thank you for the Sabbath rest. Thank you for the Sabbath. May I and my family enter into your rest on the Sabbath as you intended for us to and as you did.
            In Jesus Name
            Amen

WEDNESDAY
Scripture for Week 2

Deuteronomy 11:1
1 "You shall therefore love the Lord your God and keep his charge, his statutes, his rules, and his commandments always.

John 15:9-14
9 As the Father has loved me, so have I loved you. Abide in my love. 10 If you keep my commandments, you will abide in my love, just as I have kept my Father's commandments and abide in his love. 11 These things I have spoken to you, that my joy may be in you, and that your joy may be full.

12 "This is my commandment, that you love one another as I have loved you.13 Greater love has no one than this, that someone lay down his life for his friends.14 You are my friends if you do what I command you.

WEDNESDAY

READ:
Deuteronomy 11:1; John 15:9-14

SOAP:
Deuteronomy 11:1

Scripture

WRITE
OUT THE
SCRIPTURE
PASSAGE
FOR THE
DAY.

"you shall therefore love the Lord your God and keep His charge, His statutes, His rules, and His commandments always."

Observations

WRITE
DOWN 1 OR 2
OBSERVATIONS
FROM THE
PASSAGE.

we are to love God by keeping His charge
His statutes
His rules
His commandments
Always

WRITE
DOWN 1 OR 2
APPLICATIONS
FROM THE
PASSAGE.

We are to love God by keeping His charge (obligation), His statutes (ordinance), His rules (judgements) and His commandments (code of wisdom) always. This reminds me of when He says If you love me, you will keep my commandments (John 14:15)

Pray

WRITE OUT
A PRAYER
OVER WHAT
YOU LEARNED
FROM TODAY'S
PASSAGE.

Dear Lord,
I really want to obey you fully and love you fully! Please help me (and my family) to love you, keep your charge, your statutes, your rules and your commandments always. Thank you for your help. Love,
In Jesus' name, Amen!

THURSDAY
Scripture for Week 2

Matthew 6:25-34

25 "Therefore I tell you, do not be anxious about your life, what you will eat or what you will drink, nor about your body, what you will put on. Is not life more than food, and the body more than clothing? 26 Look at the birds of the air: they neither sow nor reap nor gather into barns, and yet your heavenly Father feeds them. Are you not of more value than they? 27 And which of you by being anxious can add a single hour to his span of life? 28 And why are you anxious about clothing? Consider the lilies of the field, how they grow: they neither toil nor spin, 29 yet I tell you, even Solomon in all his glory was not arrayed like one of these. 30 But if God so clothes the grass of the field, which today is alive and tomorrow is thrown into the oven, will he not much more clothe you, O you of little faith? 31 Therefore do not be anxious, saying, 'What shall we eat?' or 'What shall we drink?' or 'What shall we wear?' 32 For the Gentiles seek after all these things, and your heavenly Father knows that you need them all. 33 But seek first the kingdom of God and his righteousness, and all these things will be added to you.

34 "Therefore do not be anxious about tomorrow, for tomorrow will be anxious for itself. Sufficient for the day is its own trouble.

Matthew 11:28-30

28 Come to me, all who labor and are heavy laden, and I will give you rest. 29 Take my yoke upon you, and learn from me, for I am gentle and lowly in heart, and you will find rest for your souls. 30 For my yoke is easy, and my burden is light."

THURSDAY

READ:
Matthew 6:25-34; Matthew 11:28-30

SOAP:
Matthew 11:28-30

Scripture

WRITE
OUT THE
SCRIPTURE
PASSAGE
FOR THE
DAY.

"Come to me, all who labor and are heavy laden, and I will give you rest. Take my yoke upon you, and learn from me, for I am gentle and lowly in heart, and you will find rest for your souls. For my yoke is easy, and my burden is light."

Observations

WRITE
DOWN 1 OR 2
OBSERVATIONS
FROM THE
PASSAGE.

He will give us rest

He is gentle

WRITE
DOWN 1 OR 2
APPLICATIONS
FROM THE
PASSAGE.

If we come to Him when we are worried + anxious He will give us rest.
If we take on His yoke we can learn from Him b/c He is gentle and lowly of heart and His yoke is easy and His burden is light (Because He helps us carry it, Hallelujah!)

Pray

WRITE OUT
A PRAYER
OVER WHAT
YOU LEARNED
FROM TODAY'S
PASSAGE.

Dear Lord,
    Forgive me for not trusting you enough with my burdens and letting coming to you and letting you help me carry them. Lord, I'm coming to you with my burdens now and I'll take your yoke upon me b/c your yoke is easy and your burden is light. Thank you Lord for helping me! In Jesus name

FRIDAY
Scripture for Week 2

Romans 12:13
13 Contribute to the needs of the saints and seek to show hospitality.

1 Peter 4:9
9 Show hospitality to one another without grumbling.

Hebrews 13:16
16 Do not neglect to do good and to share what you have, for such sacrifices are pleasing to God.

FRIDAY

READ:
Romans 12:13; 1 Peter 4:9; Hebrews 13:16

SOAP:
Romans 12:13

Scripture

WRITE
OUT THE
SCRIPTURE
PASSAGE
FOR THE
DAY.

"Contribute to the needs of the saints and seek to show hospitality"

Observations

WRITE
DOWN 1 OR 2
OBSERVATIONS
FROM THE
PASSAGE.

- Contribute to the needs of the Saints

- Seek to show hospitality

WRITE
DOWN 1 OR 2
APPLICATIONS
FROM THE
PASSAGE.

The Lord wants us to contribute to the needs of the saints and show hospitality

Pray

WRITE OUT
A PRAYER
OVER WHAT
YOU LEARNED
FROM TODAY'S
PASSAGE.

Dear Lord,
You know it's been hard for me to show hospitality because of what's going on in my household for many years. Please make this situation better and help me to get the house de-cluttered and get the yard looking better somehow so I can welcome people here. Thank you Lord. In Jesus name, amen

61

REFLECTION QUESTIONS

1. What is the difference between fearing man and fearing God? How can you learn to fear God more than man?

   By putting Him first and revering Him more

2. What makes resting hard? What does it mean to rest in God? In what ways can you practice resting in the Lord?

   Because the enemy bombards our minds with junk, we rest in Him by keeping our minds on Him and trusting Him and having faith that He will act on our behalf.

3. Why is obedience so hard sometimes? What makes obedience hard? How does trusting God make obedience so much easier?

4. List the top three worries or uncertainties in your life. Why does God tell you not to worry? How is He faithful?

5. What is hospitality? Why is hospitality important? Is hospitality easy or hard for you? If it is hard for you, what makes it hard and what can you do to be brave in your calling to be hospitable? If it is easy for you, how often do you practice hospitality? How can you improve?

NOTES

WEEK 3

Do not be conformed to this world, but be transformed by the renewal of your mind, that by testing you may discern what is the will of God, what is good and acceptable and perfect.

ROMANS 12:2

PRAYER

WRITE DOWN YOUR PRAYER REQUESTS
AND PRAISES FOR EACH DAY.

Prayer focus for this week:
Spend time praying for your friends.

MONDAY

TUESDAY

WEDNESDAY

THURSDAY

FRIDAY

CHALLENGE

You can find this listed in our Monday blog post.

MONDAY
Scripture for Week 3

Matthew 5:10, 44

10 "Blessed are those who are persecuted for righteousness' sake, for theirs is the kingdom of heaven.

44 But I say to you, Love your enemies and pray for those who persecute you,

Romans 8:35-39

35 Who shall separate us from the love of Christ? Shall tribulation, or distress, or persecution, or famine, or nakedness, or danger, or sword? 36 As it is written,

"For your sake we are being killed all the day long;
   we are regarded as sheep to be slaughtered."

37 No, in all these things we are more than conquerors through him who loved us. 38 For I am sure that neither death nor life, nor angels nor rulers, nor things present nor things to come, nor powers, 39 nor height nor depth, nor anything else in all creation, will be able to separate us from the love of God in Christ Jesus our Lord.

Psalm 27:1

1 The Lord is my light and my salvation;
   whom shall I fear?
The Lord is the stronghold of my life;
   of whom shall I be afraid?

MONDAY

READ:
Matthew 5:10, 44; Romans 8:35-39; Psalm 27:1

SOAP:
Romans 8:35-37

Scripture

WRITE OUT THE SCRIPTURE PASSAGE FOR THE DAY.

"Who shall separate us from the love of Christ? Shall tribulation, or distress, or persecution, or famine or nakedness, or danger, or sword? As it is written,

'For your sake we are killed all day long; we are regarded as sheep to be slattered.'

No, in all these things we are more than conquerors through Him who loved us."

Observations

WRITE DOWN 1 OR 2 OBSERVATIONS FROM THE PASSAGE.

- Nothing shall separate us from the love of Christ

- We are more than conquerors through Him who loved us

Nothing will separate us from the love of Christ and we are more then conquerors through Him who loves us.

WRITE OUT
A PRAYER
OVER WHAT
YOU LEARNED
FROM TODAY'S
PASSAGE.

Dear Lord,
    Please help me to remember that nothing or no one can separate me from your love. Also, please help me to remember that I am more than a conqueror through you who loves me.
            In Jesus Name
                Amen

TUESDAY
Scripture for Week 3

2 Corinthians 9:6-8
6 The point is this: whoever sows sparingly will also reap sparingly, and whoever sows bountifully will also reap bountifully. 7 Each one must give as he has decided in his heart, not reluctantly or under compulsion, for God loves a cheerful giver. 8 And God is able to make all grace abound to you, so that having all sufficiency in all things at all times, you may abound in every good work.

Proverbs 19:17
17 Whoever is generous to the poor lends to the Lord,
   and he will repay him for his deed.

TUESDAY

READ:
2 Corinthians 9:6-8; Proverbs 19:17

SOAP:
2 Corinthians 9:6-8

Scripture

WRITE
OUT THE
SCRIPTURE
PASSAGE
FOR THE
DAY.

Observations

WRITE
DOWN 1 OR 2
OBSERVATIONS
FROM THE
PASSAGE.

Applications

WRITE
DOWN 1 OR 2
APPLICATIONS
FROM THE
PASSAGE.

Pray

WRITE OUT
A PRAYER
OVER WHAT
YOU LEARNED
FROM TODAY'S
PASSAGE.

WEDNESDAY

Romans 12:1-3

1 I appeal to you therefore, brothers, by the mercies of God, to present your bodies as a living sacrifice, holy and acceptable to God, which is your spiritual worship. 2 Do not be conformed to this world, but be transformed by the renewal of your mind, that by testing you may discern what is the will of God, what is good and acceptable and perfect.

3 For by the grace given to me I say to everyone among you not to think of himself more highly than he ought to think, but to think with sober judgment, each according to the measure of faith that God has assigned.

WEDNESDAY

READ:
Romans 12:1-3

SOAP:
Romans 12:2

Scripture

WRITE
OUT THE
SCRIPTURE
PASSAGE
FOR THE
DAY.

Observations

WRITE
DOWN 1 OR 2
OBSERVATIONS
FROM THE
PASSAGE.

Applications

WRITE
DOWN 1 OR 2
APPLICATIONS
FROM THE
PASSAGE.

Pray

WRITE OUT
A PRAYER
OVER WHAT
YOU LEARNED
FROM TODAY'S
PASSAGE.

THURSDAY
Scripture for Week 3

Ephesians 4:25
25 Therefore, having put away falsehood, let each one of you speak the truth with his neighbor, for we are members one of another.

Proverbs 12:17
17 Whoever speaks the truth gives honest evidence,
   but a false witness utters deceit.

John 17:17
17 Sanctify them in the truth; your word is truth.

THURSDAY

READ:
Ephesians 4:25; Proverbs 12:17; John 17:17

SOAP:
Ephesians 4:25

Scripture

WRITE
OUT THE
SCRIPTURE
PASSAGE
FOR THE
DAY.

Observations

WRITE
DOWN 1 OR 2
OBSERVATIONS
FROM THE
PASSAGE.

Applications

WRITE
DOWN 1 OR 2
APPLICATIONS
FROM THE
PASSAGE.

Pray

WRITE OUT
A PRAYER
OVER WHAT
YOU LEARNED
FROM TODAY'S
PASSAGE.

FRIDAY

Scripture for Week 3

2 Corinthians 4:8-9

8 We are afflicted in every way, but not crushed; perplexed, but not driven to despair; 9 persecuted, but not forsaken; struck down, but not destroyed.

Mark 10:27

27 Jesus looked at them and said, "With man it is impossible, but not with God. For all things are possible with God."

FRIDAY

READ:
2 Corinthians 4:8-9; Mark 10:27

SOAP:
2 Corinthians 4:8-9

Scripture

WRITE
OUT THE
SCRIPTURE
PASSAGE
FOR THE
DAY.

Observations

WRITE
DOWN 1 OR 2
OBSERVATIONS
FROM THE
PASSAGE.

Applications

WRITE
DOWN 1 OR 2
APPLICATIONS
FROM THE
PASSAGE.

Pray

WRITE OUT
A PRAYER
OVER WHAT
YOU LEARNED
FROM TODAY'S
PASSAGE.

REFLECTION
QUESTIONS

1. What truths help people stay strong in the midst of persecution? How should you respond to persecution because of your faith?

2. How can you be generous to others with your time and resources? Which one is harder and why? In what ways has God been generous to you?

3. What are some of the world's values that go against the teaching of Scripture? What worldly values are easy for you to compromise on? Why are the world's values and God's values sometimes so different?

4. Where do we find truth? How should understanding that God is Truth affect our trust in Him? What truths about God do you struggle to believe?

5. What discourages you? Why does God tell us not to be discouraged?

NOTES

WEEK 4

My flesh and my heart may fail,
but God is the strength of my heart
and my portion forever.

PSALM 73:26

PRAYER

WRITE DOWN YOUR PRAYER REQUESTS
AND PRAISES FOR EACH DAY.

Prayer focus for this week:
Spend time praying for your church.

MONDAY

TUESDAY

WEDNESDAY

THURSDAY

FRIDAY

CHALLENGE

You can find this listed in our Monday blog post.

MONDAY
Scripture for Week 4

Psalm 147:3
3 He heals the brokenhearted
    and binds up their wounds.

Psalm 55:22
22 Cast your burden on the Lord,
    and he will sustain you;
he will never permit
    the righteous to be moved.

Revelation 21:4
4 He will wipe away every tear from their eyes, and death shall be
no more, neither shall there be mourning, nor crying, nor pain
anymore, for the former things have passed away."

MONDAY

READ:
Psalm 147:3; Psalm 55:22; Revelation 21:4

SOAP:
Revelation 21:4

Scripture

WRITE
OUT THE
SCRIPTURE
PASSAGE
FOR THE
DAY.

Observations

WRITE
DOWN 1 OR 2
OBSERVATIONS
FROM THE
PASSAGE.

Applications

WRITE
DOWN 1 OR 2
APPLICATIONS
FROM THE
PASSAGE.

Pray

WRITE OUT
A PRAYER
OVER WHAT
YOU LEARNED
FROM TODAY'S
PASSAGE.

TUESDAY

Romans 12:1-10

1 I appeal to you therefore, brothers, by the mercies of God, to present your bodies as a living sacrifice, holy and acceptable to God, which is your spiritual worship. 2 Do not be conformed to this world, but be transformed by the renewal of your mind, that by testing you may discern what is the will of God, what is good and acceptable and perfect.

3 For by the grace given to me I say to everyone among you not to think of himself more highly than he ought to think, but to think with sober judgment, each according to the measure of faith that God has assigned. 4 For as in one body we have many members, and the members do not all have the same function, 5 so we, though many, are one body in Christ, and individually members one of another. 6 Having gifts that differ according to the grace given to us, let us use them: if prophecy, in proportion to our faith; 7 if service, in our serving; the one who teaches, in his teaching; 8 the one who exhorts, in his exhortation; the one who contributes, in generosity; the one who leads, with zeal; the one who does acts of mercy, with cheerfulness.

9 Let love be genuine. Abhor what is evil; hold fast to what is good. 10 Love one another with brotherly affection. Outdo one another in showing honor.

Psalm 73:26

26 My flesh and my heart may fail,
   but God is the strength of my heart and my portion forever.

Romans 8:26

26 Likewise the Spirit helps us in our weakness. For we do not know what to pray for as we ought, but the Spirit himself intercedes for us with groanings too deep for words.

TUESDAY

READ:
Romans 12:1-10; Psalm 73:26; Romans 8:26;

SOAP:
Psalm 73:26

Scripture

WRITE
OUT THE
SCRIPTURE
PASSAGE
FOR THE
DAY.

Observations

WRITE
DOWN 1 OR 2
OBSERVATIONS
FROM THE
PASSAGE.

Applications

WRITE
DOWN 1 OR 2
APPLICATIONS
FROM THE
PASSAGE.

Pray

WRITE OUT
A PRAYER
OVER WHAT
YOU LEARNED
FROM TODAY'S
PASSAGE.

WEDNESDAY
Scripture for Week 4

1 Peter 5:8-9
8 Be sober-minded; be watchful. Your adversary the devil prowls around like a roaring lion, seeking someone to devour. 9 Resist him, firm in your faith, knowing that the same kinds of suffering are being experienced by your brotherhood throughout the world.

1 Corinthians 10:13
13 No temptation has overtaken you that is not common to man. God is faithful, and he will not let you be tempted beyond your ability, but with the temptation he will also provide the way of escape, that you may be able to endure it.

Hebrews 4:15-16
15 For we do not have a high priest who is unable to sympathize with our weaknesses, but one who in every respect has been tempted as we are, yet without sin. 16 Let us then with confidence draw near to the throne of grace, that we may receive mercy and find grace to help in time of need.

WEDNESDAY

Scripture

WRITE
OUT THE
SCRIPTURE
PASSAGE
FOR THE
DAY.

Observations

WRITE
DOWN 1 OR 2
OBSERVATIONS
FROM THE
PASSAGE.

Applications

WRITE
DOWN 1 OR 2
APPLICATIONS
FROM THE
PASSAGE.

Pray

WRITE OUT
A PRAYER
OVER WHAT
YOU LEARNED
FROM TODAY'S
PASSAGE.

THURSDAY
Scripture for Week 4

James 1:2-4
2 Count it all joy, my brothers, when you meet trials of various kinds, 3 for you know that the testing of your faith produces steadfastness. 4 And let steadfastness have its full effect, that you may be perfect and complete, lacking in nothing.

Psalm 34:19
19 Many are the afflictions of the righteous,
  but the Lord delivers him out of them all.

THURSDAY

READ:
James 1:2-4; Psalm 34:19

SOAP:
James 1:2-4

Scripture

WRITE
OUT THE
SCRIPTURE
PASSAGE
FOR THE
DAY.

Observations

WRITE
DOWN 1 OR 2
OBSERVATIONS
FROM THE
PASSAGE.

Applications

WRITE
DOWN 1 OR 2
APPLICATIONS
FROM THE
PASSAGE.

Pray

WRITE OUT
A PRAYER
OVER WHAT
YOU LEARNED
FROM TODAY'S
PASSAGE.

FRIDAY

Scripture for Week 4

Hebrews 11:1
1 Now faith is the assurance of things hoped for, the conviction of things not seen.

2 Corinthians 4:18
18 as we look not to the things that are seen but to the things that are unseen. For the things that are seen are transient, but the things that are unseen are eternal.

Mark 9:14-24
14 And when they came to the disciples, they saw a great crowd around them, and scribes arguing with them. 15 And immediately all the crowd, when they saw him, were greatly amazed and ran up to him and greeted him. 16 And he asked them, "What are you arguing about with them?" 17 And someone from the crowd answered him, "Teacher, I brought my son to you, for he has a spirit that makes him mute. 18 And whenever it seizes him, it throws him down, and he foams and grinds his teeth and becomes rigid. So I asked your disciples to cast it out, and they were not able." 19 And he answered them, "O faithless generation, how long am I to be with you? How long am I to bear with you? Bring him to me." 20 And they brought the boy to him. And when the spirit saw him, immediately it convulsed the boy, and he fell on the ground and rolled about, foaming at the mouth. 21 And Jesus asked his father, "How long has this been happening to him?" And he said, "From childhood. 22 And it has often cast him into fire and into water, to destroy him. But if you can do anything, have compassion on us and help us." 23 And Jesus said to him, "'If you can'! All things are possible for one who believes." 24 Immediately the father of the child cried out and said, "I believe; help my unbelief!"

FRIDAY

READ:
Hebrews 11:1; 2 Corinthians 4:18; Mark 9:14-24

SOAP:
Mark 9:24

Scripture

WRITE
OUT THE
SCRIPTURE
PASSAGE
FOR THE
DAY.

Observations

WRITE
DOWN 1 OR 2
OBSERVATIONS
FROM THE
PASSAGE.

Applications

WRITE
DOWN 1 OR 2
APPLICATIONS
FROM THE
PASSAGE.

Pray

WRITE OUT
A PRAYER
OVER WHAT
YOU LEARNED
FROM TODAY'S
PASSAGE.

REFLECTION QUESTIONS

1. What is our hope in the midst of loss and grief? What comfort can you find from God's character?

2. Where do you find yourself feeling weak? How can this make you rely more on God?

3. Where do temptations usually come from in your life? How do we fight against temptations? Think of one thing that tempts you often. What are some practical things you can do to hold out and fight against it?

4. What trials are you going through right now? How can you stay strong in them? How should you handle trials that come your way?

5. What are some of your doubts? How can you overcome your unbelief and strengthen your faith?

NOTES

WEEK 5

And this is the confidence that we have toward him, that if we ask anything according to his will he hears us.

1 JOHN 5:14

PRAYER

Prayer focus for this week:
Spend time praying for missionaries.

MONDAY

TUESDAY

WEDNESDAY

THURSDAY

FRIDAY

CHALLENGE

You can find this listed in our Monday blog post.

MONDAY
Scripture for Week 5

Hebrews 10:23-25
23 Let us hold fast the confession of our hope without wavering, for he who promised is faithful. 24 And let us consider how to stir up one another to love and good works, 25 not neglecting to meet together, as is the habit of some, but encouraging one another, and all the more as you see the Day drawing near.

Proverbs 27:17
17 Iron sharpens iron,
   and one man sharpens another.

MONDAY

READ:
Hebrews 10:23-25; Proverbs 27:17

SOAP:
Hebrews 10:24

Scripture

WRITE
OUT THE
SCRIPTURE
PASSAGE
FOR THE
DAY.

Observations

WRITE
DOWN 1 OR 2
OBSERVATIONS
FROM THE
PASSAGE.

Applications

WRITE
DOWN 1 OR 2
APPLICATIONS
FROM THE
PASSAGE.

Pray

WRITE OUT
A PRAYER
OVER WHAT
YOU LEARNED
FROM TODAY'S
PASSAGE.

TUESDAY
Scripture for Week 5

John 13:34-35
34 A new commandment I give to you, that you love one
another: just as I have loved you, you also are to love one
another. 35 By this all people will know that you are my disciples, if
you have love for one another."

1 John 4:19-21
19 We love because he first loved us. 20 If anyone says, "I love
God," and hates his brother, he is a liar; for he who does not love
his brother whom he has seen cannot love God whom he has not
seen. 21 And this commandment we have from him: whoever loves
God must also love his brother.

TUESDAY

READ:
John 13:34-35; 1 John 4:19-21

SOAP:
John 13:34-35

Scripture

WRITE
OUT THE
SCRIPTURE
PASSAGE
FOR THE
DAY.

Observations

WRITE
DOWN 1 OR 2
OBSERVATIONS
FROM THE
PASSAGE.

Applications

WRITE
DOWN 1 OR 2
APPLICATIONS
FROM THE
PASSAGE.

Pray

WRITE OUT
A PRAYER
OVER WHAT
YOU LEARNED
FROM TODAY'S
PASSAGE.

WEDNESDAY
Scripture for Week 5

1 Peter 4:8-10

8 Above all, keep loving one another earnestly, since love covers a multitude of sins. 9 Show hospitality to one another without grumbling. 10 As each has received a gift, use it to serve one another, as good stewards of God's varied grace.

1 Corinthians 12:4-7

4 Now there are varieties of gifts, but the same Spirit; 5 and there are varieties of service, but the same Lord; 6 and there are varieties of activities, but it is the same God who empowers them all in everyone. 7 To each is given the manifestation of the Spirit for the common good.

WEDNESDAY

READ:
1 Peter 4:8-10; 1 Corinthians 12:4-7

SOAP:
1 Corinthians 12:4-7

Scripture

WRITE
OUT THE
SCRIPTURE
PASSAGE
FOR THE
DAY.

Observations

WRITE
DOWN 1 OR 2
OBSERVATIONS
FROM THE
PASSAGE.

Applications

WRITE
DOWN 1 OR 2
APPLICATIONS
FROM THE
PASSAGE.

Pray

WRITE OUT
A PRAYER
OVER WHAT
YOU LEARNED
FROM TODAY'S
PASSAGE.

THURSDAY
Scripture for Week 5

1 John 5:14
14 And this is the confidence that we have toward him, that if we ask anything according to his will he hears us.

Ephesians 6:18
18 praying at all times in the Spirit, with all prayer and supplication. To that end, keep alert with all perseverance, making supplication for all the saints.

Matthew 21:22
22 And whatever you ask in prayer, you will receive, if you have faith."

Luke 18:1
1 And he told them a parable to the effect that they ought always to pray and not lose heart.

THURSDAY

READ:
1 John 5:14; Ephesians 6:18; Matthew 21:22; Luke 18:1

SOAP:
1 John 5:14

Scripture

WRITE
OUT THE
SCRIPTURE
PASSAGE
FOR THE
DAY.

Observations

WRITE
DOWN 1 OR 2
OBSERVATIONS
FROM THE
PASSAGE.

Applications

WRITE
DOWN 1 OR 2
APPLICATIONS
FROM THE
PASSAGE.

Pray

WRITE OUT
A PRAYER
OVER WHAT
YOU LEARNED
FROM TODAY'S
PASSAGE.

FRIDAY
Scripture for Week 5

1 Peter 2:9
9 But you are a chosen race, a royal priesthood, a holy nation, a people for his own possession, that you may proclaim the excellencies of him who called you out of darkness into his marvelous light.

Ephesians 2:10
10 For we are his workmanship, created in Christ Jesus for good works, which God prepared beforehand, that we should walk in them.

FRIDAY

READ:
1 Peter 2:9; Ephesians 2:10

SOAP:
Ephesians 2:10

Scripture

WRITE
OUT THE
SCRIPTURE
PASSAGE
FOR THE
DAY.

Observations

WRITE
DOWN 1 OR 2
OBSERVATIONS
FROM THE
PASSAGE.

Applications

WRITE
DOWN 1 OR 2
APPLICATIONS
FROM THE
PASSAGE.

Pray

WRITE OUT
A PRAYER
OVER WHAT
YOU LEARNED
FROM TODAY'S
PASSAGE.

REFLECTION QUESTIONS

1. Why is encouragement so important? Why can encouragement be hard? How can you be more encouraging to your family and those around you?

2. What does it mean to love others? How can you love the unlovely?

3. What are some of your gifts? How are you using them to bless others?

4. How is prayer powerful? Why do we underestimate it?

5. What has God called you to be and what has He called you to do? How can we honor God in our various callings?

NOTES

WEEK 6

And God spoke all these words,
saying, "I am the LORD your God,
who brought you out of the land of
Egypt, out of the house of slavery. You
shall have no other gods before me."

EXODUS 20:1-3

PRAYER

Prayer focus for this week:
Spend time praying for yourself.

MONDAY

TUESDAY

WEDNESDAY

THURSDAY

FRIDAY

CHALLENGE

You can find this listed in our Monday blog post.

MONDAY

Scripture for Week 6

Matthew 6:33

33 But seek first the kingdom of God and his righteousness, and all these things will be added to you.

Deuteronomy 6:4-9

4 "Hear, O Israel: The Lord our God, the Lord is one. 5 You shall love the Lord your God with all your heart and with all your soul and with all your might. 6 And these words that I command you today shall be on your heart. 7 You shall teach them diligently to your children, and shall talk of them when you sit in your house, and when you walk by the way, and when you lie down, and when you rise. 8 You shall bind them as a sign on your hand, and they shall be as frontlets between your eyes. 9 You shall write them on the doorposts of your house and on your gates.

MONDAY

READ:
Matthew 6:33; Deuteronomy 6:4-9

SOAP:
Deuteronomy 6:4-6

Scripture

WRITE
OUT THE
SCRIPTURE
PASSAGE
FOR THE
DAY.

Observations

WRITE
DOWN 1 OR 2
OBSERVATIONS
FROM THE
PASSAGE.

Applications

WRITE
DOWN 1 OR 2
APPLICATIONS
FROM THE
PASSAGE.

Pray

WRITE OUT
A PRAYER
OVER WHAT
YOU LEARNED
FROM TODAY'S
PASSAGE.

TUESDAY

Exodus 20:1-3

1 And God spoke all these words, saying,

2 "I am the Lord your God, who brought you out of the land of Egypt, out of the house of slavery.

3 "You shall have no other gods before me.

Isaiah 44:6-20

6 Thus says the Lord, the King of Israel
 and his Redeemer, the Lord of hosts:
"I am the first and I am the last;
 besides me there is no god.
7 Who is like me? Let him proclaim it.
 Let him declare and set it before me,
since I appointed an ancient people.
 Let them declare what is to come, and what will happen.
8 Fear not, nor be afraid;
 have I not told you from of old and declared it?
 And you are my witnesses!
Is there a God besides me?
 There is no Rock; I know not any."

9 All who fashion idols are nothing, and the things they delight in do not profit. Their witnesses neither see nor know, that they may be put to shame. 10 Who fashions a god or casts an idol that is profitable for nothing? 11 Behold, all his companions shall be put to shame, and the craftsmen are only human. Let them all assemble, let them stand forth. They shall be terrified; they shall be put to shame together.

12 The ironsmith takes a cutting tool and works it over the coals. He fashions it with hammers and works it with his strong arm. He becomes hungry, and his strength fails; he drinks no water and is faint. 13 The carpenter stretches a line; he marks it out with a pencil. He shapes it with planes and marks it with a compass. He shapes it into the figure of a man, with the beauty of a man, to dwell in a house. 14 He cuts down cedars, or he chooses a cypress tree or an oak and lets it grow strong among the trees of the forest. He plants a cedar and the rain nourishes it. 15 Then it becomes fuel for a man. He takes a part of it and warms himself; he kindles a fire and bakes bread. Also he makes a god and worships it; he makes it an idol and falls down before it. 16 Half of it he burns in the fire. Over the half he eats meat; he roasts it and is satisfied. Also he warms himself and says, "Aha, I am warm, I have seen the fire!" 17 And the rest of it he makes into a god, his idol, and falls down to it and worships it. He prays to it and says, "Deliver me, for you are my god!"

18 They know not, nor do they discern, for he has shut their eyes, so that they cannot see, and their hearts, so that they cannot understand. 19 No one considers, nor is there knowledge or discernment to say, "Half of it I burned in the fire; I also baked bread on its coals; I roasted meat and have eaten. And shall I make the rest of it an abomination? Shall I fall down before a block of wood?" 20 He feeds on ashes; a deluded heart has led him astray, and he cannot deliver himself or say, "Is there not a lie in my right hand?"

TUESDAY

READ:
Exodus 20:1-3; Isaiah 44:6-20

SOAP:
Exodus 20:1-3

Scripture

WRITE
OUT THE
SCRIPTURE
PASSAGE
FOR THE
DAY.

Observations

WRITE
DOWN 1 OR 2
OBSERVATIONS
FROM THE
PASSAGE.

Applications

WRITE
DOWN 1 OR 2
APPLICATIONS
FROM THE
PASSAGE.

Pray

WRITE OUT
A PRAYER
OVER WHAT
YOU LEARNED
FROM TODAY'S
PASSAGE.

WEDNESDAY

Philippians 2:1-11

1 So if there is any encouragement in Christ, any comfort from love, any participation in the Spirit, any affection and sympathy, 2 complete my joy by being of the same mind, having the same love, being in full accord and of one mind. 3 Do nothing from selfish ambition or conceit, but in humility count others more significant than yourselves. 4 Let each of you look not only to his own interests, but also to the interests of others. 5 Have this mind among yourselves, which is yours in Christ Jesus, 6 who, though he was in the form of God, did not count equality with God a thing to be grasped, 7 but emptied himself, by taking the form of a servant, being born in the likeness of men. 8 And being found in human form, he humbled himself by becoming obedient to the point of death, even death on a cross. 9 Therefore God has highly exalted him and bestowed on him the name that is above every name, 10 so that at the name of Jesus every knee should bow, in heaven and on earth and under the earth, 11 and every tongue confess that Jesus Christ is Lord, to the glory of God the Father.

WEDNESDAY

READ:
Philippians 2:1-11

SOAP:
Philippians 2:3-5

Scripture

WRITE
OUT THE
SCRIPTURE
PASSAGE
FOR THE
DAY.

Observations

WRITE
DOWN 1 OR 2
OBSERVATIONS
FROM THE
PASSAGE.

Applications

WRITE
DOWN 1 OR 2
APPLICATIONS
FROM THE
PASSAGE.

Pray

WRITE OUT
A PRAYER
OVER WHAT
YOU LEARNED
FROM TODAY'S
PASSAGE.

THURSDAY
Scripture for Week 6

1 Peter 1:14-19

14 As obedient children, do not be conformed to the passions of your former ignorance, 15 but as he who called you is holy, you also be holy in all your conduct,16 since it is written, "You shall be holy, for I am holy." 17 And if you call on him as Father who judges impartially according to each one's deeds, conduct yourselves with fear throughout the time of your exile, 18 knowing that you were ransomed from the futile ways inherited from your forefathers, not with perishable things such as silver or gold, 19 but with the precious blood of Christ, like that of a lamb without blemish or spot.

THURSDAY

READ:
1 Peter 1:14-19

SOAP:
1 Peter 1:15-16

Scripture

WRITE
OUT THE
SCRIPTURE
PASSAGE
FOR THE
DAY.

Observations

WRITE
DOWN 1 OR 2
OBSERVATIONS
FROM THE
PASSAGE.

Applications

WRITE
DOWN 1 OR 2
APPLICATIONS
FROM THE
PASSAGE.

Pray

WRITE OUT
A PRAYER
OVER WHAT
YOU LEARNED
FROM TODAY'S
PASSAGE.

FRIDAY
Scripture for Week 6

Matthew 28:19-20
19 Go therefore and make disciples of all nations, baptizing
them in the name of the Father and of the Son and of the Holy
Spirit, 20 teaching them to observe all that I have commanded you.
And behold, I am with you always, to the end of the age."

Romans 10:14-15
14 How then will they call on him in whom they have not
believed? And how are they to believe in him of whom they
have never heard? And how are they to hear without someone
preaching? 15 And how are they to preach unless they are sent? As it
is written, "How beautiful are the feet of those who preach the good
news!"

FRIDAY

READ:
Matthew 28:19-20; Romans 10:14-15

SOAP:
Matthew 28:19-20

Scripture

WRITE
OUT THE
SCRIPTURE
PASSAGE
FOR THE
DAY.

Observations

WRITE
DOWN 1 OR 2
OBSERVATIONS
FROM THE
PASSAGE.

Applications

WRITE
DOWN 1 OR 2
APPLICATIONS
FROM THE
PASSAGE.

Pray

WRITE OUT
A PRAYER
OVER WHAT
YOU LEARNED
FROM TODAY'S
PASSAGE.

REFLECTION QUESTIONS

1. What keeps you from putting God first? Why is it important to put Him before all things? Why can this be scary or uncomfortable?

2. What are idols? What idols do you have in your life? What is the danger of having idols? How do we smash our idols?

3. Why is it hard to put others first? What sacrifices are required of us in order to put others first? How is Jesus our example?

4. Why are you called to be holy? Are you capable of being holy? How does Jesus help us in our pursuit of holiness?

5. What holds you back from sharing the Good News of Jesus with others? Why should we not be ashamed? How can we practice being bold?

NOTES

KNOW THESE TRUTHS
from God's Word

God loves you.
Even when you're feeling unworthy and like the world is stacked against you, God loves you - yes, you - and He has created you for great purpose.

God's Word says, "God so loved the world that He gave His one and only Son, Jesus, that whoever believes in Him shall not perish, but have eternal life" (John 3:16).

Our sin separates us from God.
We are all sinners by nature and by choice, and because of this we are separated from God, who is holy.

God's Word says, "All have sinned and fall short of the glory of God" (Romans 3:23).

Jesus died so that you might have life.
The consequence of sin is death, but your story doesn't have to end there! God's free gift of salvation is available to us because Jesus took the penalty for our sin when He died on the cross.

God's Word says, "For the wages of sin is death, but the free gift of God is eternal life in Christ Jesus our Lord" (Romans 6:23); "God demonstrates His own love toward us, in that while we were yet sinners, Christ died for us" (Romans 5:8).

Jesus lives!
Death could not hold Him, and three days after His body was placed in the tomb Jesus rose again, defeating sin and death forever! He lives today in heaven and is preparing a place in eternity for all who believe in Him.

God's Word says, "In my Father's house are many rooms. If it were not so, would I have told you that I go to prepare a place for you? And if I go and prepare a place for you, I will come again and will take you to myself, that where I am you may be also" (John 14:2-3).

Yes, you can KNOW that you are forgiven.
Accept Jesus as the only way to salvation...

Accepting Jesus as your Savior is not about what you can do, but rather about having faith in what Jesus has already done. It takes recognizing that you are a sinner, believing that Jesus died for your sins, and asking for forgiveness by placing your full trust in Jesus's work on the cross on your behalf.

God's Word says, "If you confess with your mouth that Jesus is Lord and believe in your heart that God raised him from the dead, you will be saved. For with the heart one believes and is justified, and with the mouth one confesses and is saved" (Romans 10:9-10).

Practically, what does that look like?
With a sincere heart, you can pray a simple prayer like this:

God,
I know that I am a sinner.
I don't want to live another day without embracing
the love and forgiveness that You have for me.
I ask for Your forgiveness.
I believe that You died for my sins and rose from the dead.
I surrender all that I am and ask You to be Lord of my life.
Help me to turn from my sin and follow You.
Teach me what it means to walk in freedom as I live under Your grace,
and help me to grow in Your ways as I seek to know You more.
Amen.

If you just prayed this prayer (or something similar in your own words), would you email us at info@lovegodgreatly.com?

We'd love to help get you started on this exciting journey as a child of God!

WELCOME FRIEND

*We're so glad
you're here*

Love God Greatly exists to inspire, encourage, and equip women all over the world to make God's Word a priority in their lives.

INSPIRE
women to make God's Word a priority in their daily lives through our Bible study resources.

ENCOURAGE
women in their daily walks with God through online community and personal accountability.

EQUIP
women to grow in their faith, so that they can effectively reach others for Christ.

Love God Greatly consists of a beautiful community of women who use a variety of technology platforms to keep each other accountable in God's Word.

We start with a simple Bible reading plan, but it doesn't stop there.

Some gather in homes and churches locally, while others connect online with women across the globe. Whatever the method, we lovingly lock arms and unite for this purpose…to Love God Greatly with our lives.

At Love God Greatly, you'll find real, authentic women. Women who are imperfect, yet forgiven. Women who desire less of us, and a whole lot more of Jesus. Women who long to know God through his Word, because we know that Truth transforms and sets us free. Women who are better together, saturated in God's Word and in community with one another.

Love God Greatly is a 501 (C) (3) non-profit organization. Funding for Love God Greatly comes through donations and proceeds from our online Bible study journals and books. LGG is committed to providing quality Bible study materials and believes finances should never get in the way of a woman being able to participate in one of our studies. All journals and translated journals are available to download for free from LoveGodGreatly.com for those who cannot afford to purchase them. Our journals and books are also available for sale on Amazon. Search for "Love God Greatly" to see all of our Bible study journals and books. 100% of proceeds go directly back into supporting Love God Greatly and helping us inspire, encourage and equip women all over the world with God's Word.

THANK YOU for partnering with us!

WHAT WE OFFER:

18 + Translations | Bible Reading Plans | Online Bible Study
Love God Greatly App | 80 + Countries Served
Bible Study Journals & Books | Community Groups

EACH LGG STUDY INCLUDES:

Three Devotional Corresponding Blog Posts
Memory Verses | Weekly Challenge | Weekly Reading Plan
Reflection Questions And More!

OTHER LOVE GOD GREATLY STUDIES INCLUDE:

Savior | Promises of God | Love the Loveless | Truth Over Lies
1 & 2 Thessalonians | Fear & Anxiety | James | His Name Is...
Philippians | 1 & 2 Timothy | Sold Out | Ruth | Broken & Redeemed
Walking in Wisdom | God With Us | In Everything Give Thanks
You Are Forgiven | David | Ecclesiastes | Growing Through Prayer
Names of God | Galatians | Psalm 119 | 1st & 2nd Peter
Made For Community | The Road To Christmas
The Source Of Gratitude | Esther | You Are Loved

Made in the USA
Columbia, SC
28 January 2019